This book belongs to …

....

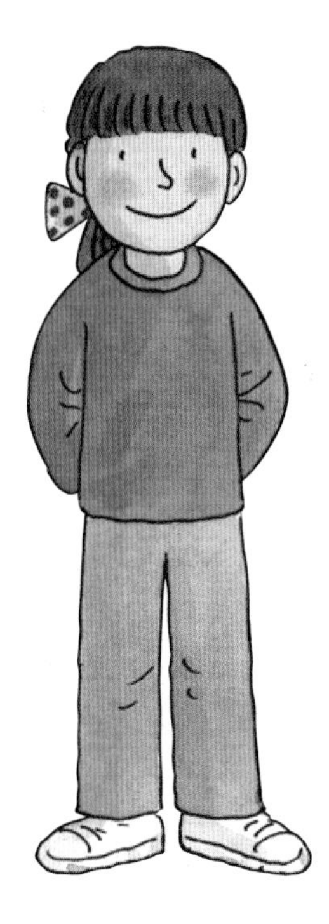

OXFORD
UNIVERSITY PRESS

Great Clarendon Street, Oxford, OX2 6DP,
United Kingdom

Oxford University Press is a department of the University of Oxford.
It furthers the University's objective of excellence in research, scholarship,
and education by publishing worldwide. Oxford is a registered trade mark of
Oxford University Press in the UK and in certain other countries

I am Kipper, It!, The Dog Tag, Cat in a Bag first published in 2007
Funny Fish, The Snowman first published in 2005
This Edition published in 2012

ISBN: 978-0-19-279399-7

1 3 5 7 9 10 8 6 4 2

Typeset in Edbaskerville

Paper used in the production of this book is a natural, recyclable product made
from wood grown in sustainable forests. The manufacturing process conforms
to the environmental regulations of the country of origin.

Acknowledgements;
Series Editors: Kate Ruttle, Annemarie Young

Funny Fish

and Other Stories

OXFORD
UNIVERSITY PRESS

Tips for Reading Together

This book has two stories: *I Am Kipper* (page 7) and *The Dog Tag* (page 19).

- Talk about the title and the picture on the cover and title pages of each story.
- Find the letters *o* and *a* in these titles and talk about the sounds they make when you read these words.
- Look at the *o* and *a* words on pages 8 and 20. Say each word and then say the sounds in each word (e.g. *Pam*, *P-a-m*).
- Read the stories and find the words with the letters *o* and *a* in them.
- Do the fun activities at the end of each story.

Children enjoy re-reading stories and this helps to build their confidence.

After you have read *The Dog Tag*, find the five toy cats in the pictures.

The main sounds practised in this book are 'o' as in *dog* and 'a' as in *cat*.

For more hints and tips on helping your child become a successful and enthusiastic reader look at our website www.oxfordowl.co.uk.

I am Kipper

Written by Roderick Hunt
Illustrated by Nick Schon,
based on the original characters
created by Roderick Hunt and Alex Brychta

Read our names

I am Kipper.

I am Pam.

I am Mat.

I am Pat.

I am Tom.

I am Mac.

I am Sam.

Sam
Pat
Mat
Mac
Tom
Pam

Talk about the story

Who did what?

Match each child with the right word.

tap

mop

hop

pop

The Dog Tag

Written by Roderick Hunt
Illustrated by Nick Schon,
based on the original characters
created by Roderick Hunt and Alex Brychta

Read these words

got cat

top cap

pot mat

mop tag

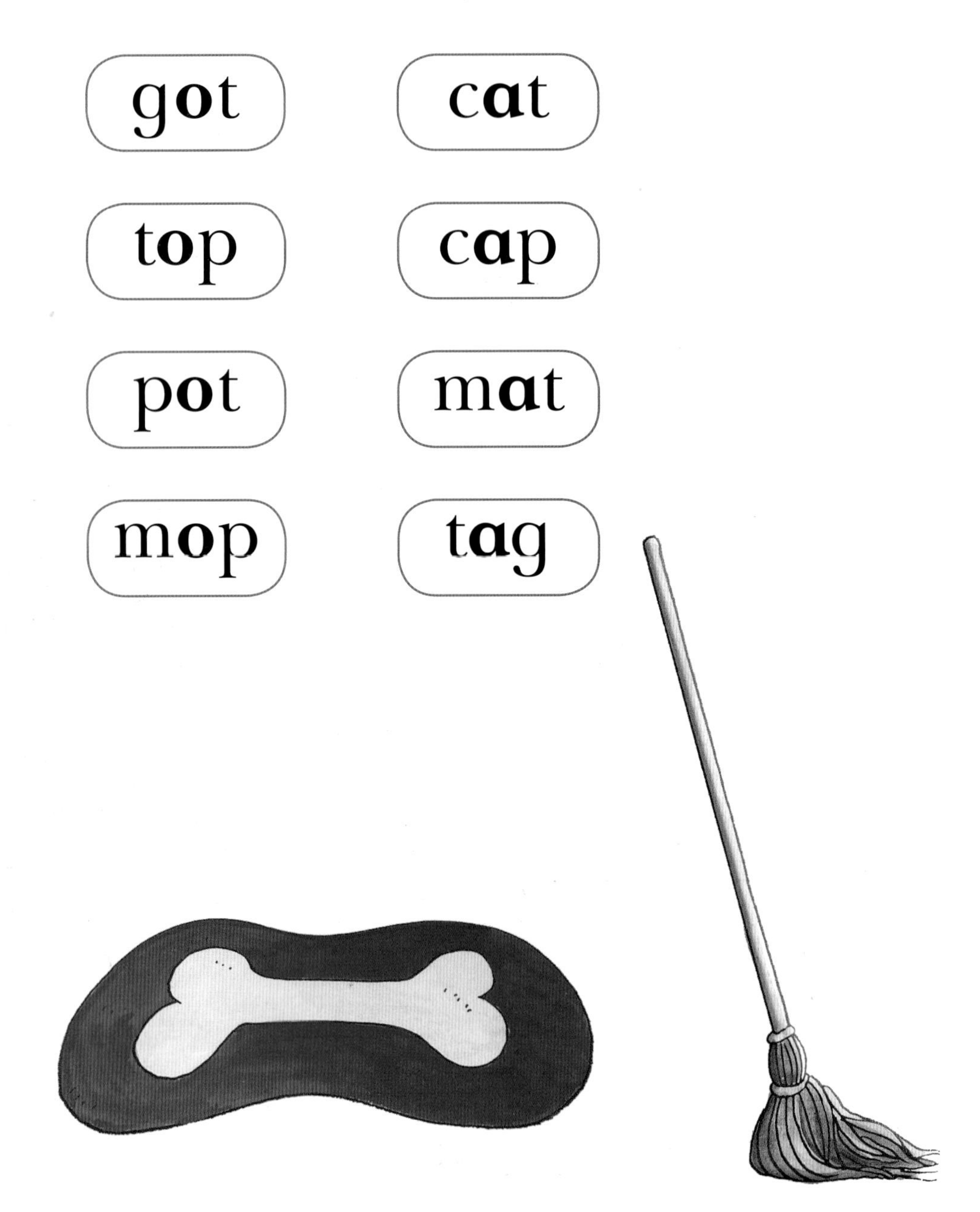

Kipper got a cat.

Biff got a top.

Chip got a cap.

Mum got a pot.

Dad got a mop.

Floppy got a mat.

Floppy got a tag.

Floppy sat on the mat . . .
. . . and he got a pat.

Talk about the story

Tips for Reading Together

This book has two stories: *Cat in a Bag* (page 31) and *It* (page 43).

- Talk about the title and the picture on the front cover and title pages of each story.
- Find the letters *a* and *i* in these titles and talk about the sounds they make when you read them in these words.
- Look at the *a*, *i* and *u* words on pages 32 and 44. Say the sounds in each word and then say each word (e.g. *t-i-n*, *tin*).
- Read the stories and find the words with *a*, *i*, *o* and *u*.
- Do the fun activities at the end of each story.

Children enjoy re-reading stories and this helps to build their confidence.

Have fun!

After you have read *It*, find five birds in the pictures.

The main sounds practised in this book are 'a' as in *bag*, 'i' as in *tin*, and 'u' as in *tub*.

For more hints and tips on helping your child become a successful and enthusiastic reader look at our website www.oxfordowl.co.uk.

Cat in a Bag

Written by Roderick Hunt
Illustrated by Nick Schon,
based on the original characters
created by Roderick Hunt and Alex Brychta

OXFORD
UNIVERSITY PRESS

Read these words

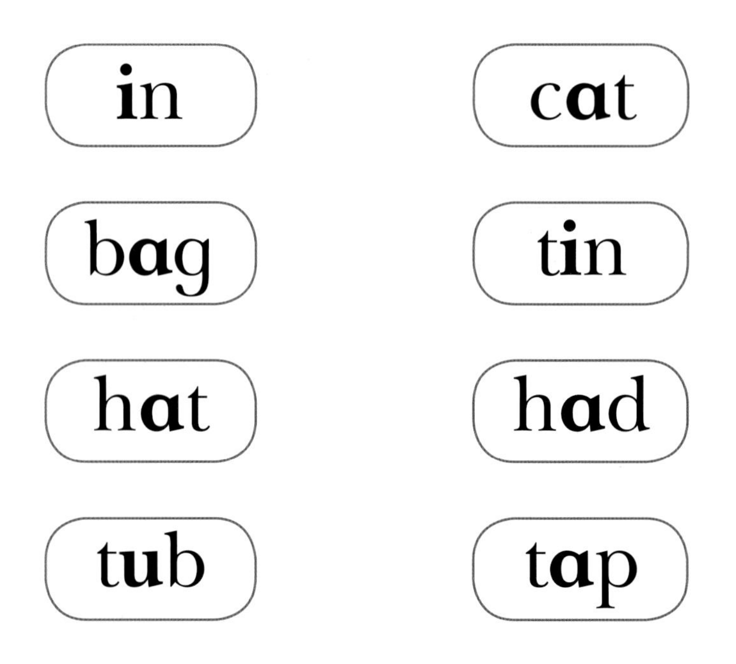

i**n**

c**a**t

b**a**g

t**i**n

h**a**t

h**a**d

t**u**b

t**a**p

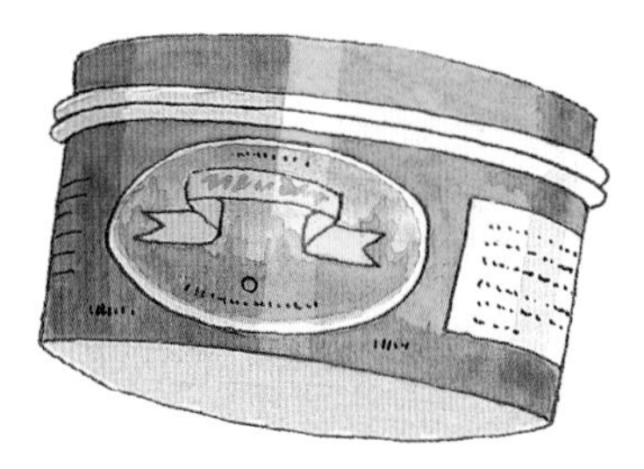

Wilf had a cat.
He put a hat on the cat.

Wilf had a bag.
He put the cat in the bag.

tap, tap, tap

Wilf had a tub.
He put the bag in the tub.

tap, tap, tap

Wilf had a tin.
He put the tub in the tin.

tap, tap, tap

Wilf had the cat in his hat.

Talk about the story

Missing letters

Choose the letter to make the word.

c ___ t

W ___ lf

t ___ n

h ___ t

It

Written by Roderick Hunt
Illustrated by Nick Schon,
based on the original characters
created by Roderick Hunt and Alex Brychta

OXFORD
UNIVERSITY PRESS

Read these words

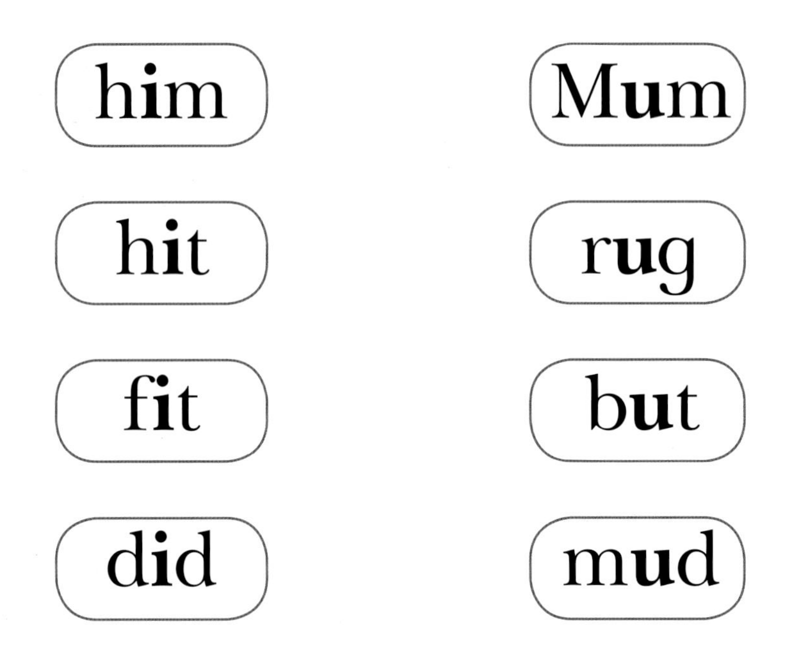

Chip put on the cap.
He was ‘it’.

Mum ran and Kipper ran.
Mum got on the box.

Kipper got on the rug.

Biff ran.
She got on the box.

Dad ran, but Chip got him.

Dad put on the cap.
It did not fit.

Bam! Dad ran into Floppy.

Dad hit the mud.

Talk about the story

Tips for Reading Together

Children learn best when reading is fun.

- Talk about the title and the picture on the front cover.
- Look through the pictures together so your child can see what the story is about.
- Read the story to your child, placing your finger under each word as you read.
- Read the story again and encourage your child to join in.
- Give lots of praise as your child reads with you.

Children enjoy re-reading stories and this helps to build their confidence.

Have fun!

After you have read the story,
find the starfish hidden in every picture.

This book includes these useful common words:
got he she was

For more hints and tips on helping your child become a successful and enthusiastic reader look at our website www.oxfordowl.co.uk.

Funny Fish

Written by Cynthia Rider
based on the original characters
created by Roderick Hunt and Alex Brychta
Illustrated by Alex Brychta

OXFORD
UNIVERSITY PRESS

Mum Dad Biff

Chip Kipper Floppy

Kipper was fishing.

He got a hat.

Biff was fishing.

She got a crab.

Chip was fishing.

He got an octopus!

Mum was fishing.

She got a bucket.

Dad was fishing.

He got a boot.

SPLASH!

Floppy got a fish!

Talk about the story

Tips for Reading Together

Children learn best when reading is fun.

- Talk about the title and the pictures on the cover.
- Look through the picture together so your child can see what the story is about.
- Read the story to your child, placing your finger under each word as you read.
- Read the story again and encourage your child to join in.
- Give lots of praise as your child reads with you.

Children enjoy re-reading stories and this helps to build their confidence.

After you have read the story, find the robin hidden in every picture.

This book includes these useful common words:
had it no

For more hints and tips on helping your child become a successful and enthusiastic reader look at our website www.oxfordowl.co.uk.

The Snowman

Written by Cynthia Rider,
based on the original characters
created by Roderick Hunt and Alex Brychta
Illustrated by Alex Brychta

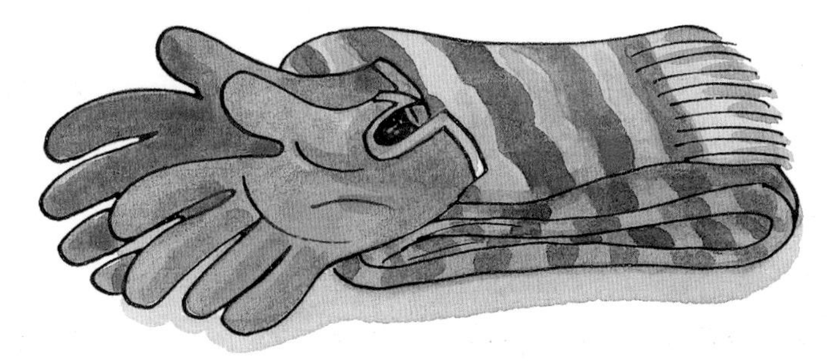

OXFORD
UNIVERSITY PRESS

Biff Chip Wilma

Wilf Kipper Floppy

Wilma made a snowman.

It had a red nose.

It had a blue scarf.

It had green gloves.

It had a black hat.

The hat fell on Floppy.

Floppy ran.

Oh no!

No snowman!

Talk about the story

Fun activity

Find the twin snowmen.